THE GREAT HAIR RESTART

THE GREAT HAIR RESTART

*The Ultimate Guide to Resetting Your Natural Hair
Journey with Confidence*

KAREN HILL

J MERRILL

J Merrill Publishing, Inc.
434 Hillpine Drive
Columbus, OH 43207
www.JMerrill.pub

Library of Congress Control Number: 2023924577
ISBN-13: 978-1-961475-12-0 (eBook)
ISBN-13: 978-1-961475-13-7 (Paperback)
ISBN-13: 978-1-961475-14-4 (Hardback)

Book Title: The Great Hair Restart
Author: Karen Hill
Cover Artwork: Safeer Ahmed

TABLE OF CONTENTS

WELCOME TO THE JOURNEY OF SELF-DISCOVERY AND SELF-LOVE THROUGH HAIR TRANSFORMATION

INTRODUCTION

IN THIS BOOK, I offer you an opportunity to embark on a life-changing journey of self-discovery and self-love by exploring the depths of your hair. With over thirty-seven years of experience guiding individuals toward hair transformation, I am excited to share my knowledge with you.

Over the years, I have worked with many clients who have achieved incredible transformations in their relationship with their hair. Their stories and experiences have inspired me to help others embrace their unique hair journeys. Now, they eagerly await your transformation, excited to see its impact on your life.

Based on my extensive experience, I will guide you through understanding and loving your hair. Together, we will challenge societal norms and beliefs surrounding hair, paving the way for a paradigm shift in your perception.

Through my journey as a young girl and the countless individuals I have worked with, I will share stories and lessons that will resonate with you. In addition, I will provide you with a comprehensive understanding of how hair works, empowering you to develop a new hair routine that aligns with your newfound perspective.

By the end of this book, you will understand why your hair behaves the way it does, giving you the tools to confidently manage issues such as curling, straightening, growth, and scalp care.

A COMPREHENSIVE GUIDE TO HAIR TRANSFORMATION

Transforming your hair is a process that requires time and dedication. It usually takes about a year to grow a new head of hair, but the benefits are immeasurable. By following the journal and embracing the thirty-day challenge of implementing a new hair routine, you will witness a remarkable transformation in your hair and other areas of your life. You will gain insight into why your hair behaves the way it does and why issues like lack of consistent curl pattern, scalp issues, or that you don't understand or like your hair.

PONDERING A LIFE WITHOUT HAIR-RELATED CONCERNS

Have you ever thought about leading a life free of hair-related issues? Imagine not worrying about upkeep, feeling confident, or even learning to swim. How would you define yourself if hair posed no problem?

Take a moment to consider how not understanding your hair has affected your life. Think about three instances where you feel your hair has held you back.

WHAT SETS THIS BOOK APART

This book is not your typical hair styling guide. It caters to both stylists and clients alike. While stylists excel at creating stunning hairstyles, knowing how to maintain your hair at home is imperative. If you're experiencing hair loss, thinning, or heat damage, it's your responsibility to take care of it because it's your hair! Clients who understand their hair's needs are more satisfied with their overall look. You'll learn what I've discovered and shared with countless others in this book.

Important Note: This book should provide guidance and knowledge on natural hair care and styling. However, it is crucial to understand that I am not a medical doctor. As a hairstylist, my expertise lies in hair care and styling techniques.

It is essential to recognize that certain situations may require the attention of a qualified healthcare professional. Suppose you have any underlying medical conditions or concerns related to your scalp or hair that go beyond hairstyling. In that case, I strongly advise you to seek the expertise of a doctor or dermatologist. They can provide a proper diagnosis, treatment, and guidance based on their medical training and experience.

While this book aims to empower you with knowledge and techniques for caring for your natural hair, it is important to use common sense and exercise caution. If you encounter any unusual symptoms, discomfort, or worsening of your condition, it is advisable to discontinue any practices and seek professional advice.

SECTION 1: WHAT TO EXPECT

Book Expectations:

- Anticipate significant changes in your hair care routine.
- Refrain from using chemical relaxers throughout the process.
- Avoid keratin treatments or other substances that could impact your hair's natural state.
- As a fair warning, there is no middle ground - even minor touch-ups around the edges are not recommended.

IT'S A SLOW PROCESS

The Frustration of Slow Hair Growth: This process can be slow and discouraging. It takes a full year to grow a new head of hair, and there are no shortcuts to speed up the process. While it can be tempting to use texturizers or relaxers, staying motivated by setting goals and reminding yourself that patience is key is essential.

THAT'S NOT DAMAGE

Understanding the Line of Demarcation When Transitioning to Natural Hair: During the transition to natural hair, you'll notice a clear line that separates your damaged ends from your new, natural growth. This is called the line of demarcation. While it's the weakest point on each hair strand, shifting your mindset and viewing it as new hair growth rather than breakage is important. Although blending the two textures is challenging, effective communication with your support group or hair ambassador can help you navigate this transition period.

DON'T BE DISCOURAGED

When transitioning to natural hair, you may experience some breakage or a complete transformation of your hair texture. It's crucial to understand that we're focusing on the new growth, not the hair on your head that's already damaged. Don't be discouraged if you don't see immediate results and continue to treat your hair with care. I will not recommend excessive products or over-conditioning, as the new hair is entirely different. Remember that everyone goes through this process, and during the first three months, it may feel like your hair is going backward. Don't lose hope and give up—stay committed to your hair journey.

BUILDING A ROUTINE

Creating a Healthy Haircare Routine

I am here to assist you in establishing a healthy haircare routine that suits your lifestyle. To achieve optimal results, I strongly recommend using Synergi products. Follow these simple steps to care for your hair:

- Shampoo your hair thoroughly until it is clean.
- Use a shampoo that deeply cleanses your hair and does not leave toxic residue. Wash your hair at least once a week.
- Trim your hair every eight to ten weeks to gradually remove split ends.
- Avoid overloading your hair with products that merely coat the strands.

By following these basic steps, you will be able to restore the health of your hair in no time!

WHO'S YOUR HAIR CRUSH

Tips for Healthy Natural Hair

Your heart knows what your hair needs to flourish. Follow these steps to find your hair type, and search Pinterest for a photo that closely matches the look and feel you desire.

CONSIDER WHAT YOU WANT TO EXPERIENCE

Consider what you want to experience: swimming, working out, vacation, peace, freedom, and style. Embrace and love your hair for what it is and be honest about its capabilities. Remember to accept others' journeys, as everyone's path is unique. Set goals beyond physical appearance, as how you want to feel is just as crucial. Remember to always strive for something more significant than yourself.

AVOID SOCIAL MEDIA

For hair transitioning, my approach is one-of-a-kind and distinct from anything you'd find on blogs or YouTube. The method is based on my extensive experience and proven results. I have taught clients and stylists this same method for over thirty-seven years. While many bloggers write about transitioning to natural hair, few have executed it. That's why it may seem confusing, but completing this book will give you the clarity you need. Trust me, it's worth it!

TUNE OUT NEGATIVE PEOPLE

- Remember that this book is one of a kind, and not everyone will understand why you invested in it. Consider keeping it to yourself and watch as people notice your positive changes.
- Don't feel the need to convince others of the value of this challenge. People can be skeptical or unsupportive, so it's best to show them the benefits through your actions.
- Be cautious of DIY advice, as it may lead to confusion.
- Stay true to your goals, and don't let anyone discourage you, especially those unhappy with their path.

By following these tips, you'll be able to connect the dots and make the most of your course experience.

FIND A BRAND AMBASSADOR

To further support your journey, connect with our Synergi brand ambassadors. They are experienced and dedicated supporters and advocates of Synergi Systems and Products. You can find them on our Facebook Page, Synergi Salon, Facebook private group Synergi Salon Journey to Natural, and Synergi Lifestyle on YouTube.

MY FINAL TIP

The most important one is to love your hair and yourself! Enjoy the journey! You get to discover your natural hair slowly, and it's one of the most exciting things you can do for yourself. Don't forget to seek tips, advice, and encouragement from other naturals or people you trust.

THE POWER OF POSITIVE THINKING FOR NATURAL HAIR

Believe it or not, your thoughts significantly impact your hair. Your mental, spiritual, and physical state all work together to create something greater than the sum of its parts. When one component is affected, it impacts the others equally. This is the essence of synergy—all things working together to create a greater outcome.

Take your hair, for example. If you don't like your natural hair, you may unconsciously think and speak negatively about it. However, your thoughts respond to your words, and the universe makes whatever you speak possible. What if you changed your thinking and how you talked about your hair?

Great natural hair begins with how you feel, think, and speak about it. You must believe in your heart that your hair can thrive and prosper. But it's not just about believing—you also need to put in the work to give your hair the best opportunity to thrive.

Reaching your hair goals doesn't have to be difficult. It takes a good plan, a healthy mindset, and a community of like-minded individuals to see it through to the finish line—freedom, confidence, and peace.

Negative attitudes can hinder your opportunity for a successful transition, so having a positive mindset is essential. Here are a few tips to help you think positively about your natural hair:

- Recognize how you think matters.
- Positive thinking brings positive results.
- Understand why positive thinking is essential.
- Learn how to think positively about your natural hair.

- Avoid negative thoughts, as they bring similar results.
- Find ways to stop negative thinking.

Remember, the power of positive thinking can work wonders for your hair and your overall well-being. So, let's start thinking positively and watch our hair flourish!

Chapter Two

SHADES OF BEAUTY: CHALLENGING COLORISM AND HAIR STEREOTYPES

IN A FAMILY PORTRAIT

As a child, I recall my hair being quite lovely in photos. My family members and others often complimented me for having long, beautiful hair and being an adorable little girl. Despite being timid and reserved, my hair was my greatest asset and a source of pride.

This book section aims to remind readers of their natural hair state before it becomes problematic. Often, people with thick hair or a lot of hair resort to relaxers, thinking it will make their life easier. The assumption is that having less hair to manage or untangle is better. However, forcing hair to conform to a specific look doesn't improve it; it just makes it thinner and weaker. Remember, less is not always better.

Life in the 70s and 80s differed vastly from today's modern era. Back then, most homes lacked central air, making it quite uncomfortable inside, especially after a fresh hairdo. Once your hair was styled, you couldn't do much without ruining it. Swimming or tampering with your hair for at least two weeks was forbidden. I believe, therefore, that many Black women wash their hair every two weeks—a practice that can be traced back to that era.

Now, looking back at family history is the best way to determine what your hair type really is. People often comment, "I have my mother's hair in the front and my father's hair in the back." That comes from genetics—yes, hair is passed down most times. But not only texture but also routine. So, if the texture is different and your mom was used to a particular routine, and your texture was different, it would make things problematic. So, I suggest looking back at generations to see textures, routines, and rituals.

A Family Portrait and Reflection on Colorism

In this photo, my grandmother, mom, and aunt stand together, with my mom in the middle. As a young girl, my mother had a darker complexion than the rest of the family. This is where colorism comes into play—assuming that skin tone and hair texture are inherently linked. However, my mother defied this stereotype. Despite her brown skin, her hair was silky-straight.

On my mother's side were individuals with light skin and long, straight hair, while on my father's side (who was from Warren, Ohio) had brown or darker skin tones. Reflecting on how society historically viewed light skin as "good" and brown skin as "bad," I realized how this bias influenced my perception of my hair, leading me to believe it was inadequate.

Nurturing Our Roots: Reflections on Childhood Haircare and Forgiving the Past

When I was a baby, my hair was always stunning and attracted attention. People would gush over how adorable I looked, and my hair made me stand out. However, my hair became thicker, longer, and stronger as I grew older. With these changes, it became increasingly challenging to manage. I struggled with the tender care and maintenance of my hair!

Do you have memories of your hair as a child? Can you recall any specific routines or care practices before you started getting any chemical services or encountered issues with your hair?

If you don't remember your hair before getting relaxers, it could be a sign that your mom had a lot on her plate and had to resort to certain measures. It's important to understand that in those days, we didn't have the same tools and modern conveniences that we have now. It's essential to forgive her because she did the best she knew how to do with the resources available.

Many people feel upset when they think about their moms putting relaxers in their hair at an early age. However, it's crucial to consider the circumstances and limitations of that era. Let's acknowledge our moms' challenges and extend forgiveness, knowing they did what they believed was best for us.

WASH DAY WOES: CONFRONTING CHILDHOOD TRAUMA AND RECLAIMING HAIRCARE CONFIDENCE

Once a simple task, wash day became a haunting experience that filled me with dread. The local children of various ages, races, and genders became an audience to my anguish, finding fascination in my torment.

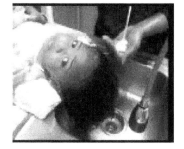

Their eyes gleamed with curiosity as they witnessed the tears and heard my anguished cries. Their twisted amusement deepened my self-consciousness and vulnerability, making me feel like a pitiful spectacle.

The memory of wash day still haunts my mind like a recurring nightmare. From the moment my mother cleared the sink, a sense of foreboding settled upon me. I was overwhelmed and scared but ready to get my hair done at the same time.

Chapter Three

SCARS OF BEAUTY: THE TRAUMA OF HAIR RELAXATION AND THE QUEST FOR SELF-ACCEPTANCE

AT THE TENDER age of six, an ominous decision was made that would forever alter the course of my hair journey. My unsuspecting innocence was shattered as my mother, driven by the allure of societal beauty standards, subjected my precious hair to the treacherous process of hair relaxation.

Excitement coursed through my veins as I envisioned myself with sleek, straight hair, like the glamorous models in magazines and on television. Little did I know that this innocent desire would lead me down a path of torment. Before applying the relaxer, my mom would carefully grease or base my hair and scalp to protect it from burning. Though the greasy feeling was not my favorite, I endured it for the promise of the result: manageable, silky hair. As my mom sectioned my hair, I closed my eyes, cherishing the moments of bonding and self-care.

The application of the relaxer brought searing pain to my delicate scalp, as if fiery tendrils were snaking through my hair follicles. The once-protected edges now bore scars and scabs, constant reminders of the agony I endured. But none of that mattered because getting my hair straight was more important than how I felt.

Fear gripped my heart, preventing me from scratching or touching my tender scalp, as it would unleash a fresh wave of torment. The relentless itchiness became a cruel reminder of the price I paid for pursuing an unattainable beauty ideal.

A Tale of Hair Struggles and a Father's Disapproval

One day, my father walked into the living room and saw my mother applying a chemical relaxer to my precious curls.

Disappointment and concern filled his eyes as he questioned the necessity of altering my naturally beautiful hair. He understood the importance of embracing our roots and preserving our identity, which he knew was directly linked to my self-esteem. He was absent during the arduous process of washing and styling my hair, making it difficult for him to comprehend fully the daily struggles I faced.

Life Was Great After the Relaxer

In this captivating photograph, taken the day after my first relaxer, the transformation of my hair is apparent. My edges lay sleek and straight, radiating joy and contentment. I couldn't contain my excitement, eagerly posing for the camera in my adorable outfit. It was picture day, a momentous occasion where memories were captured, and I was thrilled because my hair looked effortlessly smooth and uncomplicated.

The newfound straightness of my hair brought a sense of confidence and delight. It was a tangible representation of the possibilities that lay ahead, a glimpse into a world where my hair could conform to societal standards of beauty. At that moment, I felt a surge of happiness and anticipation for the future.

FIRST GRADE

In this cherished photograph, I am transported back to my first-grade year, where my hair held special significance. It was during this time that my mother took charge of styling my hair, ensuring it always looked beautiful and healthy. Her skill and dedication were evident, and I felt confident and content as long as she was in control.

However, as time passed, relaxers' availability expanded beyond licensed hairdressers. This newfound accessibility brought both excitement and trouble into my life. My mom made good decisions about relaxing my hair, but I took charge when I got older. So, if once was good, more had to be better. While the initial results of using relaxers were excellent, with my hair looking sleek and polished, constant touch-ups and maintenance began to spiral out of control.

In my quest for hair inspiration, I found myself drawn to the iconic character of Little Penny, portrayed by the talented Janet Jackson. Her hairstyle exuded confidence, style, and a sense of empowerment that resonated deeply within me. I yearned to recreate that same aura, to embody the essence of Little Penny's captivating presence.

With determination fueling my every step, I embarked on a journey to transform my hair into a reflection of the beauty I admired. Studying every detail of Little Penny's hairstyle, I became determined to achieve a look that exuded strength and individuality. Throughout this journey, I experienced moments of frustration and self-doubt. However, I persevered, recognizing that true inspiration lies not in replicating someone else's appearance but in finding the courage to express our authentic selves.

TRAPPED IN THE LYE: MY JOURNEY OF DENIAL AND HAIR DAMAGE

As a young Black girl, I found myself trapped in a cycle of denial, refusing to acknowledge the damage that the lye relaxer was causing to my hair. Blinded by its initial satisfaction, I failed to see the long-term consequences. My hair and I suffered along with it, yearning for the days when my natural hair was healthy and beautiful.

Looking back, I now recognize that a harmful addiction ensnared me. The relaxer had become a crutch, a false sense of beauty that I clung to despite the apparent damage it inflicted.

FRUSTRATED AND YEARNING: MY BATTLE WITH HAIR DAMAGE IN FIFTH GRADE

As I grew older, I noticed changes in my peers and how boys seemed to overlook me. Deep down, I couldn't help but wonder if my hair was the reason. Despite this thought lingering in my mind, I held onto the belief that my long, pretty hair would return one day. However, my hair continued to worsen, and I realized I needed to take matters into my own hands.

In this chapter, I took charge of my hair journey, as my mom was no longer involved. Frustration fills my heart as I confront the reality of my damaged hair and the impact it has on my self-esteem.

12th Grade

Once I got to my twelfth-grade year, my hair was in shambles. I had cut it too short, colored it too much, and relaxed it for too long. At this point, I thought my hair would never grow. I believed that my hair would always be short, and it never dawned on me that getting a chemical process was why my hair wasn't changing.

It was like being in a toxic relationship and never realizing that the relationship wasn't working. That's how I viewed chemical processing and relaxing. It was a relationship that no longer served me, but I had no idea that the relaxer or the chemical was the problem. So, I continued doing the same thing over and over.

FROM DAMAGE TO CREATIVITY: EMBRACING ICONIC HAIRSTYLES OF THE 90S

In the 90s, Salt-N-Pepa's hair was a major inspiration for many, including myself. Little did I know that their iconic hairstyles were likely a result of damaged and over-processed hair, just like mine. We didn't have the luxury of weaves to enhance our styles, so we had to make the most of what we had.

It's fascinating to think about how this trend emerged from a place of necessity. Chemical treatments had damaged our hair, and instead of resorting to drastic measures like shaving it all off, we got creative. We worked with what we had left, experimenting with different styles and techniques.

Salt-N-Pepa was the perfect example. See how one side is shaved and the other side is short? It looks like a style, but it's actually in recovery. It's a cool save. But you would think we would stop here. But no.

BREAKING FREE FROM THE WEAVE: UNVEILING THE TRUTH BEHIND HAIR DAMAGE AND EMBRACING NATURAL BEAUTY

For years, I found myself trapped in a cycle of relying on weaves and protective styles to compensate for my lifeless and damaged hair. Growing up as a Black woman in the 90s, it seemed like the norm to turn to weaves and relaxers as the solution to our hair struggles. But as I reached age twenty, a profound realization shook me and completely shifted my perspective.

Back in the day, purchasing hair weave was a meticulous process that required careful measurement by the inch to achieve the desired style, whether it be bangs or length. Blending the weave with our natural hair took great patience and skill. It's remarkable to think that despite the toxic nature of this practice, it was still quite common. We had yet to understand that the relaxer was the primary cause of the toxic hair issues. We continued to use it. And when our hair inevitably fell out, we resorted to using weaves as a temporary solution.

The Significance of Relaxer Treatments in Our Hair Care Routines

In the past, getting a relaxer was a crucial aspect of our hair care routines, particularly for special occasions. We believed achieving straight and sleek hair was the key to the perfect look, regardless of the damage, dye, or previous treatments our hair had undergone. According to the instructions on the back of the box, the recommended time frame for getting a relaxer was to re-apply to new growth every six weeks for all hair types. However, the ideal was only to relax the new growth, which was less than an eighth of an inch. This led to overlapping during the application of the relaxer, which ultimately resulted in hair thinning and falling out.

BREAKING FREE FROM CHEMICALS: DISCOVERING THE POWER OF NATURAL HAIR

My hair was short during the transition, and I embraced this length for a few years. It was a liberating experience as I discovered the beauty and versatility of short, natural hair. However, as time passed, I contemplated growing my hair out, curious to explore the possibilities of longer styles.

But I realized that the more I relaxed my hair, the limper and weaker it was. When I needed a relaxer, my hair felt strong and thick. I made a conscious decision to get off the merry-go-round. It's so funny because

I kept quiet about it. I thought I'd be ridiculed and challenged about why my hair was too good for chemicals. Yes, I was afraid to hear "Oh, you got good hair" remarks, and that's why you can grow your relaxer out.

Now, I was a stylist and worked around hair daily. I could tell my hair was nothing like my clients'. My clients would get their hair done and last until their next visit. They had thick, beautiful hair. My hair would be a mess the next day. I could not use oils, greases, or heavy sprays. Paying someone to do my hair was a waste of money. Mine was limp and flat. I thought natural hair wasn't for everyone. I decided to stop. NOW!

I also noticed that when I shampooed my hair, I liked my hair better. I kept shampooing as often as I could. I was a stylist, so I understood my hair in ways most of my life did not. I kept doing that for many years. I'd shampoo in the morning before work and at night after work. I continued this process for years. My hair was worn straight. I could wash my hair, straighten and wrap it, and my hair would be cute.

HEALING FROM WITHIN: OVERCOMING ECZEMA AND DISCOVERING HOLISTIC SOLUTIONS

I battled with severe eczema throughout my life, and as I grew older, the breakouts became even more relentless. The eczema appeared on my face, arms, and legs, causing immense discomfort and frustration. While I had learned to cope with it as a child, the condition seemed to worsen over time, possibly because of factors like diet and stress.

I exercised in my quest for relief, hoping it would provide some respite. However, to my dismay, I discovered that sweating during workouts only exacerbated my skin condition. The sweat would linger on my skin, triggering more intense flare-ups. Realizing the detrimental impact of sweat on my eczema, I incorporated a new routine into my life.

After each workout, I prioritized shampooing my hair, not necessarily every day, but as frequently as possible. This simple act helped prevent sweat from lingering on my skin, providing some relief from the flare-ups. Surprisingly, shampooing my hair became a source of solace that no medicine could replicate. I vividly recall visiting a doctor who suggested that the chemicals from working with hair might aggravate my condition, even suggesting that I consider a different career. Desperate for a holistic solution, I was determined to find a way to heal from within.

This chapter delves into my journey of overcoming eczema and discovering holistic solutions. From adjusting my exercise routine to finding relief through hair shampooing, I explore the transformative power of addressing the root causes of my condition and embracing a holistic approach to healing.

BEYOND HAIR TYPES: EMBRACING UNIQUE HAIR JOURNEYS AND THE POWER OF DEDICATION

While working at a salon located within a gym, I had the opportunity to observe and learn from women of diverse backgrounds and hair types. One particular encounter stands out in my memory.

One day, as I was finishing my workout before starting my shift, I noticed a woman with beautiful, long, flowing white hair. She caught my attention because she seemed to spend significant time styling her hair after her workout. Intrigued, I mustered the courage to approach her and initiate a conversation.

I asked her how long it took her to style her hair every morning after exercising. To my surprise, she replied it took her a full hour. I was amazed by her dedication and commitment. She explained she allocated that time because it allowed her to focus on her hair entirely. She accepted that if she wanted to work out, it came with the responsibility of dedicating time to styling her hair afterward.

This encounter completely changed my perspective. I had always believed that women with specific hair types had it easier regarding hair care. However, this woman's story shattered that misconception. It taught me that everyone has a unique hair journey regardless of hair type. Sometimes, it requires a significant investment of time and effort.

Inspired by her story, I adopted a similar approach. I realized that the more time and attention I dedicated to my hair, the easier it became to manage. I learned that taking the time to care for and style my hair was not a burden but an act of self-care and self-expression.

This encounter with the woman at the gym salon truly transformed my outlook on hair care. It taught me the importance of dedication and commitment, regardless of hair type or texture. It reminded me that we all have unique hair journeys, and it is through embracing and investing in them that we can truly appreciate and celebrate our individuality.

HAIR TRANSFORMATIONS: EMBRACING CHANGE, FINDING CONVENIENCE, AND PRIORITIZING SELF-CARE

In search of a convenient solution for managing my hair during workouts, I incorporated wigs into my daily routine. This included wearing a wig every day, even at the gym. After each workout, I would exchange the wig for a fresh one, repeating this pattern for several months. This approach proved more convenient than dealing with my natural hair, but I remained committed to maintaining the cleanliness and freshness of my hair and the wigs.

To ensure that my hair and wigs remained fresh and odor-free, I established a daily routine of washing my hair underneath the wig. This practice became essential in preventing any lingering sweat or unpleasant odors from transferring to the new wig. By diligently washing my hair every day, I prioritized hygiene and kept my natural hair and the wigs in optimal condition.

The desire for convenience drove me to wear wigs during workouts and easily manage my hair. It allowed me to focus on my fitness goals without the added stress of styling or dealing with the aftermath of sweaty workouts. By embracing wigs as a practical solution, I maintained a polished appearance while prioritizing my health and fitness.

Throughout this period, I learned the importance of adaptability and finding solutions that work best for our individual circumstances. While wearing wigs may not be the choice for everyone, it provided me with the convenience and flexibility I needed during that time. It served as a reminder that self-care is a personal journey, and sometimes, we need to explore unconventional methods to find what works best for us.

Ultimately, my commitment to cleanliness and freshness ensured that my hair and wigs remained in excellent condition. This allowed me to pursue my fitness goals confidently while maintaining a polished appearance. The experience taught me the value of finding practical solutions that align with our lifestyles, empowering us to prioritize our well-being without compromising our style. I found a routine, but it got hard. I underwent many changes—silk press, cutting, letting it grow, chopping it off.

UNVEILING THE CURLS: EMBRACING NATURAL HAIR AND THE JOURNEY TO SELF-DISCOVERY

However, my wig routine was tested when my family and I visited Florida. The scorching heat made me realize the wig would be unbearable to wear. I realized nobody in Florida knew me, so I felt free to make a change.

Upon arriving at the hotel, I asked my cousin if she had any mousse. I quickly worked some finger curls into my hair, though the ends remained straight. Then I went to the front desk, borrowed a pair of scissors, and snipped off the straight pieces. That was the first time I saw my hair curl naturally. It was a revelation. For the last fifteen years, I've been embracing my natural curls.

But as I embraced my natural curls, I realized my hair had so much more potential. I discovered that letting it grow out allowed me to experiment with different styles and lengths I never thought possible. Not only that, but I also found that taking care of my curls became self-care. It was a way to connect with my natural beauty and feel confident in my skin. Now, I have a collection of products and techniques to enhance my curls and keep them healthy and beautiful. I've even inspired some of my friends to embrace their natural hair textures and start their curly hair journeys. It's incredible how something as simple as embracing your natural curls can positively impact your life.

BEYOND THE CUT: EMBRACING LIBERATION AND DEFYING EXPECTATIONS WITH SHORT HAIR

Short haircuts have always been my go-to. I remember turning down a blind date once because I hadn't styled my hair that day. My date thought I wasn't interested and canceled future plans, leaving me feeling disappointed. I was frustrated with myself for allowing my hair to hold me back. It was around the time when Britney Spears famously shaved off her hair that I did the same. Since then, whenever I felt overwhelmed with my hair, I embraced the challenge and shaved my hair all off. And I repeated this cycle for fifteen years.

I learned a lot about myself and my relationship with my hair then. I realized I had been using my hair as a crutch, relying on it to make me feel pretty and confident. But when I finally let it all go, I felt a sense of liberation I had never experienced. It was as if I had shed a layer of insecurities and self-doubt along with my hair.

Of course, not everyone was supportive of my decision. Some people thought I was crazy, while others assumed I was going through some crisis. But I didn't care. I knew that my short haircuts symbolized my strength and independence, and that was all that mattered.

Now, as I look back on those fifteen years of short haircuts, I realize they were more than just hairstyles. They were statements expressing my individuality and refusing to conform to society's expectations. And I'm proud of myself for having the courage to embrace that.

Chapter Four

SHARING KNOWLEDGE ON NATURAL HAIR CARE WITH WOMEN

THROUGHOUT THE YEARS, I have spoken at diverse settings like churches, living rooms, schools, and basements. I have aimed to teach and share knowledge with women about loving and embracing their natural hair. I am passionate about empowering women to feel confident and beautiful.

WHAT YOU'LL DISCOVER: A GUIDE TO HEALTHY HAIR

1. Determine your hair type and its unique needs. Different hair types require specific care, and analyzing your hair's texture, porosity, and density can help you determine the ideal products and methods to employ.
2. Create a hair care routine that fits your way of life, including washing, conditioning, and styling. If you're short on time, choose low-maintenance hairstyles that are simple to maintain.
3. Challenge your preconceptions about your hair and find a stylist eager to assist you in understanding your hair thoroughly.

4. Learn how to choose high-quality hair products free of harmful chemicals specifically formulated for your hair type.

5. Embrace your natural hair and experiment with different styles and products to find what works best for you, whether you prefer to wear your hair curly, straight, or in a protective style.

GET READY TO TRANSFORM YOUR LIFE: WHAT TO EXPECT ON THIS JOURNEY

By the end of this journey, you will have achieved the following benefits for yourself:

- Work out with no worries.
- Travel freely and confidently.
- Save money.
- Experience more flexibility with your hair.
- Enjoy swimming without any hassle.
- Receive gratitude from your significant other.
- No more hair frustration.
- Handle scalp problems with ease.

Thank you for considering this journey. Have a great day.

THE POWER OF REFLECTION: MAXIMIZING YOUR JOURNEY THROUGH JOURNALING

Keeping a journal is crucial to track progress and understand your journey. Here are some tips to make the most out of your journal:

- Be consistent.
- Be honest.
- Reflect on your journey.
- Celebrate your successes.

Use your journal to identify areas of struggle and stay focused on your goals. Trust the process and remain committed to your journey.

Achieving Versatile, Healthy Hair with the "Curly-2-Straight" Method

The Curly-2-Straight method is a technique that uses flat irons, blow dryers, and other heat-styling tools to straighten hair while maintaining its natural curl pattern. This approach prioritizes proper hair care, heat protection, high-quality tools and products, a consistent wash day routine, and a solid understanding of your hair.

What sets this method apart is its ability to teach individuals how to manage their curly hair while still allowing them to straighten it as desired, making it easy to switch between styles.

EMPOWERING BLACK HAIR: BREAKING BARRIERS, EMBRACING BEAUTY, AND CHALLENGING MISCONCEPTIONS

- Black women face unique challenges in caring for their natural hair, such as hair loss, damage, and breakage.
- Education and resources on natural hair care can help Black women properly care for their hair, embrace natural beauty, and challenge harmful beauty standards and misconceptions.
- Black hair is not inherently unmanageable or difficult to style, and natural hair is just as professional as any other hair type.
- Chemical treatments like relaxers are unnecessary for "good" hair and can be harmful.
- Regular washing is crucial for maintaining healthy hair and scalp.
- When done correctly, protective styles like braids and weaves can promote hair growth and health.
- Black hair is versatile and can be styled in many ways with no heat.
- Additionally, it's essential to support initiatives like the Crown Act, which works to end discrimination based on hairstyle.

In my journey to promote equality and inclusivity, I introduced a resolution declaring racism as a public health crisis in the City of Columbus. Recognizing the significance of hair in the Black community, I am proud to have championed the inclusion of provisions in the Columbus City Code that acknowledge the importance of race and protective and cultural hairstyles. These provisions aim to combat discrimination in areas such as employment, fair housing, public accommodations, and even criminal acts committed in schools. With the support of my colleagues and the administration, we are working towards creating an inclusive culture that embraces and appreciates the beauty and diversity of Black hair. Together, we can break barriers, celebrate our culture, and challenge discrimination based on hairstyle.

EMPOWERING THE BLACK DOLLAR: UNVEILING THE INFLUENCE AND NURTURING THE BEAUTY OF BLACK HAIR

The power of the Black dollar in the hair care industry is undeniable. Black women have long been the largest consumers of hair products, spending significant money on maintaining and styling their hair. This consumer power has created a lucrative market that caters specifically to the unique needs of Black hair.

Interestingly, while other cultures may have a small section dedicated to hair products for their specific hair types, Black women often have entire aisles or dedicated stores solely catering to their hair needs. This speaks to Black women's immense demand and purchasing power in hair care.

The Black hair care industry has evolved, with a wide range of products specifically formulated for Black hair textures and styles. From shampoos and conditioners to styling creams, gels, and oils, a vast array of options are available to cater to the diverse needs of Black hair.

However, this abundance of products can also lead to a phenomenon known as "product junkie-ism." Many Black women constantly search for the next best product to solve their hair concerns. This can cause a cycle of excessive product consumption, where individuals spend significant money trying different products, hoping to find the perfect solution.

This cycle of product consumption can be attributed to a lack of education and understanding about Black hair. Society, including the beauty industry, has not always prioritized teaching Black women about their hair and its unique needs. This lack of knowledge can leave Black women feeling lost and reliant on trial and error in finding the right products for their hair.

However, the tide is slowly shifting. More and more Black women are seeking to educate themselves about their hair, its needs, and the best ways to care for it. Books, online resources, and communities dedicated to natural hair care have emerged, providing valuable information and empowering Black women to make informed choices about their hair care routines.

By understanding our hair and its unique needs, Black women can break free from the cycle of excessive product consumption. We can focus on nurturing and celebrating our natural hair, embracing its beauty and versatility without constantly chasing the next best product.

The power of the Black dollar in the hair care industry lies in our purchasing power and ability to demand better representation, education, and understanding. As we continue to support brands and businesses that prioritize our needs and empower ourselves with knowledge, we can drive positive change within the industry and celebrate the beauty of Black hair.

Chapter Five

UNLOCKING THE SECRETS OF HAIR: ANATOMY, CUTICLE CARE, DEMARCATION, AND HAIR TYPES

THIS SECTION DELVES into the intricacies of hair, including its anatomy, the line of demarcation, factors that lead to an unhealthy cuticle, and the various hair types. Understanding hair anatomy and types is essential for proper hair care and styling.

Objective: Upon completing this section, you will be able to:

- Understand the structure of hair.
- Identify healthy and unhealthy cuticles.
- Recognize the line of demarcation.
- Define hair types.
- Appreciate the importance of knowing hair anatomy and types.

Lessons:

1. Hair Anatomy and Its Function
2. Cuticle Health and Maintenance
3. The Line of Demarcation and Its Significance
4. Hair Typing and Its Applications
5. Understanding Hair Density
6. Appreciating Hair Texture

UNVEILING THE WONDERS OF HAIR: FUNCTIONS, PROTECTION, AND SELF-EXPRESSION

- **Exploring the Fascinating World of Hair:** Hair is a unique characteristic of mammals that serves several vital purposes. Today, let's delve into the functions of hair and why it's so important to us.

- **Regulating Body Temperature:** Hair helps regulate our body temperature by creating an insulating layer of air when we're cold. The tiny muscles attached to each hair follicle contract, causing the hair to stand up and trap air that helps keep us warm.

- **Protection from Environmental Factors:** Hair protects our skin from the sun and other environmental factors, acting as a natural sunscreen on our scalp and as a barrier against dirt, bacteria, and other irritants on other parts of our bodies.

- **Self-Expression:** Hair is functional and crucial to our identity and self-expression. Our hair's style, length, and color can communicate who we are, our creativity, individuality, and cultural heritage. Now that we understand the significance of hair, let's dive deeper into the fascinating world of hair.

DECODING THE HAIR: AN IN-DEPTH EXPLORATION OF ITS COMPONENTS AND FUNCTIONS

- **The Hair and Its Different Components: A Comprehensive Overview:** Let's delve into the various components of hair and their respective functions.
- **The Hair Shaft:** This is the visible part of the hair that emerges from our skin. Made up of keratin, a protein, the hair shaft protects our scalp and skin.
- **The Sebaceous Gland:** Attached to the hair follicle, this gland produces sebum, an oil that helps keep our hair and skin moisturized and is essential for optimal hair health.
- **The Arrector Pili Muscle:** This muscle causes hair to stand up straight when cold or scared. Its contraction results in the "goosebumps" effect, which can help trap warm air close to the skin.
- **The Hair Bulge:** A small region at the base of the hair follicle that contains stem cells necessary for hair growth and the regeneration of new follicles.
- **The Hair Follicle:** The pocket where hair grows from is connected to the blood supply by the papilla, providing the hair with nutrients and oxygen necessary for growth.
- **The Hair Bulb:** Located at the base of the hair follicle, it contains cells that divide rapidly to create new hair cells. These cells push the older ones up and out of the skin.
- **The Hair Capillary:** A small blood vessel that supplies the hair with nutrients and oxygen necessary for optimal hair growth and health.

As we can see, each component of the hair plays a crucial role in its overall health and growth. Understanding these distinct parts allows us to better care for our hair and keep it looking beautiful and healthy.

- **The Hair Strand:** The visible part of the hair that extends above the surface of our skin. It comprises three layers: the cuticle, the cortex, and the medulla.

UNLOCKING THE SECRETS OF HAIR STRUCTURE: EXPLORING THE CUTICLE, CORTEX, MEDULLA, AND KERATIN FOR OPTIMAL HAIR CARE

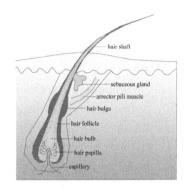

- **Hair Structure: Understanding the Cuticle, Cortex, Medulla, and Keratin:** Hair care has become an essential part of our daily lives. Understanding hair structure can help us take better care of our hair and keep it looking healthy and beautiful.
- **The Cuticle:** The outermost layer of the hair strand. It acts as a protective barrier for the inner layers of the hair and is composed of overlapping scales that keep the hair shaft smooth and prevent damage. Knowing the importance of the cuticle can help us maintain our hair's health and avoid issues such as frizziness, breakage, and dullness.
- **Cortex:** The thickest and most important layer of the hair shaft. It gives the hair its strength, flexibility, and elasticity. The cortex also contains pigment granules called melanin that provide hair color.
- **Medulla:** The innermost layer of the hair shaft. It is not present in all hairs and can vary in size and shape. The medulla contributes to the overall texture and thickness of the hair.
- **Keratin:** The main structural component of hair, nails, and the outer layer of skin in mammals. It comprises amino acids, including cysteine, methionine, arginine, and serine. Cysteine contains a sulfur atom that can form strong chemical bonds with other cysteine molecules, creating disulfide bridges that give keratin strength and durability.

In summary, understanding the different parts of the hair strand and the composition of keratin can help us make informed choices when selecting hair care products and practices that promote healthy, beautiful hair.

UNLOCKING THE SECRETS TO HEALTHY, BEAUTIFUL HAIR: UNDERSTANDING CUTICLES, POROSITY, AND OPTIMAL HAIRCARE

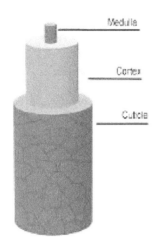

As we delve into the world of hair care, it becomes clear that the health of our cuticles plays a vital role in maintaining the beauty and vitality of our hair. By comprehending the distinction between a healthy hair cuticle and a damaged one and understanding how it relates to hair porosity, we can effectively nurture and care for our hair. Let's explore further:

The cuticle, forming the outermost layer of the hair shaft, acts as a protective barrier for the inner layers of our hair. Our hair appears healthy and vibrant when the cuticle is smooth and intact. However, damaged cuticles exhibit raised scales that cannot lie flat against each other, resulting in hair that appears rough, lackluster, and prone to frizz, breakage, and split ends.

Hair porosity refers to the hair's ability to absorb and retain moisture and is directly influenced by the health of our cuticles. High-porosity hair absorbs excessive moisture, leading to frizz, tangling, and breakage. Damaged cuticles often contribute to high porosity. On the other hand, low-porosity hair is more resistant to moisture absorption and retention. Healthy cuticles are typically associated with low porosity.

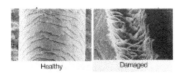

By gaining a deeper understanding of the intricate relationship between hair cuticles and porosity, we can adopt effective hair care practices that cater to the specific needs of our hair. This knowledge empowers us to maintain our hair's optimal health and appearance, ensuring it remains beautiful and vibrant.

Navigating the Line of Demarcation for Healthy, Beautiful Hair

Embarking on transitioning from chemically treated or relaxed hair to natural hair can be both exciting and challenging. One key aspect to understand during this process is the line of demarcation, where natural hair meets previously treated hair. As I grow out my natural hair, I notice that the line of demarcation gradually moves down my hair shaft as the new hair grows in at the roots.

This area requires special care and attention to prevent breakage and damage. I have learned that avoiding harsh chemicals and heat styling tools is essential to protect this delicate section. By treating my hair gently and being patient, I allow the line of demarcation to continue moving down my hair shaft, eventually reaching a point where all the chemically treated or relaxed hair can be trimmed away, leaving me with only natural hair. Understanding the line of demarcation has been crucial in my hair care journey, helping me achieve healthy, beautiful locks while transitioning to natural hair.

DEALING WITH TWO TEXTURES AND THE LINE OF DEMARCATION: TIPS & TRICKS

If you're struggling with two distinct hair textures, here are some tips to help manage it:

- **Cutting it Down:** It's best to wait until you're comfortable with the length of your hair when it's not stretched out before cutting it. This usually takes about three months.
- **Blow Drying:** If you use heat, blow dry your hair and straighten the new growth to match the ends. Once it's matched, you can continue using heat as desired.

- **Styling:** Wearing your hair in curly styles can be challenging when your roots vary significantly from your ends. It's best to avoid natural hair sets until your natural hair has fully grown out. Protective styles can be a suitable alternative but be careful because hair can snap where the line of demarcation is.
- **Protective Styles:** When using protective styles, cutting your ends aggressively while wearing them is essential. You may need to leave your protective style in longer until you're comfortable taking it down and dealing with your natural hair.

MAINTAINING HEALTHY CUTICLES: FACTORS THAT IMPACT THEIR HEALTH AND HOW TO CARE FOR THEM

Unlocking the Secrets to Healthy, Beautiful Hair: Understanding Cuticles, Porosity, and Optimal Haircare

Factors that can affect the health of your cuticles: The cuticles on your hair and nails play an integral role in keeping them healthy. Here are some factors that can impact their health:

1. **Stress:** Elevated stress levels can cause hormonal imbalances and damage hair and nails. Poor sleep can also contribute to unhealthy cuticles.
2. **Poor Diet:** A lack of essential vitamins and minerals, such as biotin, vitamin E, and zinc, can cause brittle cuticles.
3. **Harsh Chemicals:** Exposure to harsh chemicals in some relaxers and removers can strip natural oils from your cuticles, making them dry and prone to breakage.
4. **Overuse of Heat Tools:** Heat tools like hair dryers and flat irons can cause damage to your hair and cuticles, increasing the risk of breakage.

5. **Environmental Factors:** Extreme temperatures, like cold winter air and hot summer sun, can also contribute to unhealthy cuticles.

6. **Lack of Proper Care:** Neglecting regular shampooing, trimming, or caring for your hair can lead to unhealthy cuticles.

To keep your cuticles healthy and strong, practice good hygiene, avoid harsh chemicals and environmental factors, eat a balanced diet, manage stress levels, and limit the use of heat styling tools.

HAIR TYPING

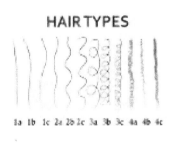

HAIR TYPES

1a 1b 1c 2a 2b 2c 3a 3b 3c 4a 4b 4c

Understanding Hair Typing: A Useful Tool for Natural Hair Care Hairstylist Andre Walker developed the concept of hair typing to categorize hair based on texture and curl pattern. The system uses numbers and letters to identify hair texture, ranging from 1A (straight hair) to 4C (tight, coily hair). While hair typing can help you select the right products and styles for your hair, it's important to remember that it's not a perfect system. Hair texture can vary within each category, and every individual's hair is unique.

Hair typing has become popular in the natural hair community as people seek to better understand and care for their hair. You can choose the best products and styles by understanding your hair's texture and curl pattern. However, it's crucial to listen to your hair's needs and not get too caught up in the hair typing system.

Hair typing is just one way to describe hair and is not a definitive measure of hair health or beauty. The most important thing is to choose products and styles that work best for you, regardless of your hair type. So, while hair typing can be a valuable tool in understanding your hair, it's essential to remember that your hair's unique needs should always come first.

UNDERSTANDING HAIR TYPES: STRAIGHT, WAVY, CURLY, AND KINKY

Hair has four basic types: straight, wavy, curly, and kinky. Knowing your hair type can help give it the care and attention it needs to look its best. Here's a quick rundown of each hair type:

- **Straight Hair:** Smooth, shiny, and lacks texture. It's easy to manage but may be challenging to hold curls or add volume.
- **Wavy Hair:** Has a slight S-shape, giving it more volume and texture than straight hair. It can range from gentle waves to more pronounced curls.
- **Curly Hair:** Features a more defined S-shape or spiral pattern, giving it lots of texture and volume. It can range from loose curls to tight coils.
- **Kinky Hair:** Exhibits a tight, zigzag pattern, providing the most texture and volume of all hair types. It can range from tightly coiled to more loosely curled.

To determine your hair type, examine the shape of your hair strands. If they're straight, you have straight hair. If they have a gentle S-shape, you have wavy hair. You have curly hair if it has a more defined S-shape or spiral pattern. And if they have a tight zigzag pattern, you have kinky hair.

Each hair type has its unique characteristics and challenges. For example, people with wavy hair may struggle with frizz, while those with curly hair may need special products to keep their curls hydrated. By understanding your hair type, you can choose the right products, tools, and techniques to keep your hair healthy and looking its best.

AN INTRODUCTION TO GENETICS:

- **Genetics:** The science that studies how traits are passed down from one generation to the next.
- **Genes:** Made up of DNA, which contains the instructions for growth and function.
- **Inheritance:** During reproduction, organisms pass down half of their genes to their offspring.
- **Traits:** Inherited genes result in traits that can be physical or behavioral.
- **Physical Traits:** Include eye color or height.
- **Behavioral Traits:** Include personality or intelligence.
- **Single vs. Multiple Genes:** Some traits are determined by a single gene, while multiple genes influence others.

Simplified Explanation:

- **Genetics:** Like a recipe book that tells your body how to grow and function.
- **Inheritance:** You get half of your recipe book from your mom and half from your dad.
- **Traits:** Sometimes you inherit a trait from one parent and not the other, such as having blue eyes from your mother and brown hair from your father.
- **Gene Control:** Some traits are controlled by one recipe, while others by many working together.

HAIR DENSITY: UNDERSTANDING HAIR DENSITY, THICKNESS, AND TEXTURE

Hair density refers to the number of hair follicles in a given scalp area. This can vary depending on genetics, age, and overall health and is usually calculated by the number of hairs per square inch of the scalp. The average hair density for most people is around 2,200 hairs per square inch, but it can range from as low as 1,000 hairs per square inch to as high as 4,000 hairs per square inch.

It's important to note that hair density is different from hair thickness. Hair thickness refers to the diameter of each hair strand and can vary from person to person. Hair thickness can also be classified as coarse or thin, affecting its overall appearance and texture.

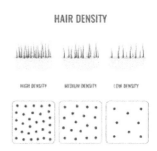

Hair texture is another important factor to consider in hair care and styling. People with coarse hair may require different products and techniques than those with thin hair. Understanding your hair's unique texture is essential, as this will help determine the best methods for maintaining and styling it.

Hair density, thickness, and texture are all important factors to consider when it comes to hair care. Understanding these concepts can help you choose the right products and techniques for your hair, ensuring it looks and feels its best.

UNDERSTANDING HAIR TYPES: COARSE VS. FINE HAIR

Hair density refers to the number of hair follicles in a given scalp area. This can vary depending on genetics, age, and overall health and is usually calculated by the number of hairs per square inch of the scalp. The average hair density for most people is around 2,200 hairs per square inch, but it can range from as low as 1,000 hairs per square inch to as high as 4,000 hairs per square inch.

HAIR TEXTURE

The width of a single strand of hair

COARSE   NORMAL   FINE

It's important to note that hair density is different from hair thickness. Hair thickness refers to the diameter of each hair strand and can vary from person to person. Hair thickness can also be classified as coarse or thin, affecting its overall appearance and texture.

Hair texture is another important factor to consider in hair care and styling. People with coarse hair may require different products and techniques than those with thin hair. Understanding your hair's unique texture is essential, as this will help determine the best methods for maintaining and styling it.

Hair density, thickness, and texture are all important factors to consider when it comes to hair care. Understanding these concepts can help you choose the right products and techniques for your hair, ensuring it looks and feels its best.

Understanding Hair Elasticity

Hair elasticity refers to the ability of a strand of hair to stretch and then return to its original state. To determine your hair's elasticity, wet a section of hair and stretch it as much as possible. By comparing the texture of new hair growth to the rest of your hair, you can easily identify any differences in elasticity.

UNLOCKING THE POWER OF SEBUM: HARNESSING THE BENEFITS OF NATURAL OILS FOR HEALTHY HAIR

The Effects of Oil on the Hair

- Why some products don't work on natural hair.

Discover the Importance of Your Natural Oils and How to Use Them in This Lesson: Have you ever been told that frequently shampooing your hair will strip it of natural oils? Let's put that myth to rest and learn about the crucial role of your natural oils and how to activate them for your benefit.

The Sebaceous Gland Understanding the Role of Sebaceous Glands in Skin and Hair Health: Sebaceous glands are small glands in the skin that secrete an oily or waxy substance called sebum. This lubricates both the skin and hair of mammals. The sebum is secreted into hair follicles and eventually reaches the skin's surface, where it mixes with sweat. The resulting mixture forms a protective layer known as the acid mantle. This waxy, acidic oil acts as a barrier to protect both hair and skin. Interestingly, sebum coats hair even before it emerges from the scalp.

- **The Benefits of Sebum: How It Can Transform Your Hair:** The majority of hair challenges addressed in this course are related to our cuticles. Complete sebum coverage can solve these problems for one main reason: sebum is 100% organic and moderately hydrophobic, stabilizing the moisture your hair retains. The pH of sebum flattens your hair cuticle, which is why your hair looks and behaves better when wet–the curl pattern is visible, and it's easier to style and detangle without causing breakage. However, once your hair dries, it can feel rough, and the curl may disappear. Complete sebum coverage prevents this by maintaining many of the benefits of wet hair when dry. Your curl pattern will be more visible and flexible, and your hair can withstand manipulation without breaking. Overall, your hair will look and feel better throughout the day.
- **Dealing with Wet vs. Dry Hair: Tips for Styling During This Course:** Style your hair when wet for the best results. Avoid styling when it becomes too dry, which can damage your hair. If your hair gets too dry, re-wet it before styling. It's best to style your hair immediately after washing it.
- **Sweat and Sebum: The Symbiotic Relationship:** Sweat and sebum have a unique bond. The acidic pH of sweat or

the heat and moisture it produces breaks down sebum, allowing it to slide down the hair strand easily. However, cleaning the hair with shampoo at least once a week is essential.

- **Steam Treatments: Revitalizing Your Hair:** At Synergi Salon, we offer deep steam sessions to our clients. Steam helps lift cuticles and enhance moisture retention for several days. However, if you have complete sebum coverage, there's less need to disturb the cuticle. While deep steam sessions can be beneficial occasionally, they won't be necessary as often with full sebum coverage.
- **The Root Cause of Dry Hair:** Many people believe their hair is extremely dry and continuously apply creams and oils to coat the hair. However, this issue also exists in shampoos, conditioners, styling products, sweat, and a lack of shampooing. Protective hairstyles can contribute to this problem. The purpose of sebum is to protect and strengthen the hair, but when the hair is heavily coated, it cannot penetrate the constant application of silicone. The more product buildup, the weaker the hair becomes, leading to dryness. It's essential to rebuild the hair from the ground up.

- **Why Hair Puffs Up When Straightened:** When straightening natural hair, product buildup is often the primary culprit for hair not staying straight. If someone shampoos infrequently, suggest they switch to shampooing at least once a week. After a few weeks, try straightening the hair 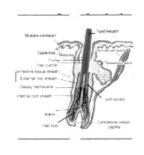 again and notice the difference. It's typically a game-changer, and the hair straightens more easily.
- **Transitioning to Protective Styles: Protecting Weak Ends:** Switching to protective styles can be harsh on fragile ends, and extensive trimming may be necessary. During this transitional period, ask your stylist to cut your hair into a

shape that will help avoid further damage. It's okay to cut more than usual each time.

GROWING OUT WEAVES AND BRAIDS: LEARNING FROM A HAIR CARE COURSE WHILE WEARING PROTECTIVE STYLES

Wearing protective styles should not hinder your ability to learn from this course. Once you take down your protective style, you can implement what you've learned throughout the year. It's recommended that you trim your ends each time you take your  protective style down before putting it back up into another protective style. Try leaving your hair out of the protective style for a bit longer each time you take it down, using this example:

- 0-3 months: cut hair and return it immediately in a protective style.
- 3-6 months: cut hair and wait one week before putting it back in a protective style.
- 6-9 months: cut hair and wait a few weeks before putting it back in a protective style.
- 9-12 months: wait as long as possible before putting your hair back in a protective style.

It's extremely difficult to properly care for your hair and scalp while wearing protective styles.

PROPER HAIR CARE: THE IMPORTANCE OF PROPER HAIR CARE

Protective styles were initially designed to allow you to switch up your hairstyle. However, they are only intended for temporary use and should not be worn for extended periods. This is important for children whose hair is still developing. Ensuring that you properly care for your hair can help prevent long-term damage.

Chapter Six

4 STAGES OF REGROWING YOUR HAIR

ENDURING THE STAGES OF HAIR GROWTH: WHY UNDERSTANDING THE PROCESS IS KEY

Knowing how your hair grows can make all the difference in preparing for each stage of growth. While it may be challenging, anticipating potential difficulties can help you brace yourself and take the necessary steps to progress successfully. Understanding these stages and their impact on your hair health and styling options is essential for a smooth transition during your hair care journey.

1. The "New Birth" Stage: 0-3 Months

You're just beginning to transition from chemically treated to natural hair during this stage.

Here are some helpful tips to keep in mind:

- The hair may be very dry at this stage, particularly at the roots.
- Be excited about what's coming but try not to overwhelm yourself with too much information or product purchases.
- Shampooing your hair weekly will make it easier to manage, softer, and more manageable.
- It's too early to determine your hair type since hair continues to change rapidly.
- Don't worry about styles lasting long, as the hair changes quickly at this stage.
- Be prepared to ask your stylist to cut your hair if needed.
- If you typically straighten your hair, continue to do so since curly styles are difficult until your hair is completely natural. (Your hair will be straight at the ends and curly at the roots.)
- The goal during this stage is to shampoo your hair at least once a week, or more if possible.
- Keep a journal to document your challenges and successes with building your shampoo routine.
- Avoid some protective styles, as they can be harsh on weak ends.

3. The "Pit" Stage: 3-6 Months

This stage is infamously known as "The Pit" in your hair journey, where your new growth roots show. Styling your hair will become a struggle, and you might complain to anyone who will listen. Don't panic; this is normal. You've come too far to turn back now. Though the line of demarcation may make it seem like your hair is falling out, remember that you're making space for new hair to grow. This is a huge mindset shift. You may also notice that any scalp conditions you previously battled with will begin to clear up. Your shampoo routine may not be perfect, but the goal is to shampoo your hair weekly and take a deep breath.

4. The Breakaway Stage: Months 6-9 of Hair Growth

Between the sixth and ninth months is what we call the Breakaway Stage. This is when you'll see new growth sprouting all over your head, more than you've seen in a while. However, avoid wearing your hair in curly styles at this stage because you'll still be dealing with two different textures. Though it's exciting to see progress, managing your hair daily can still be challenging.

But don't worry, there's hope! You'll stop complaining and embrace your hair for what it is. You'll feel a sense of accomplishment and pride. Your scalp will be free of dryness and dandruff. By now, the goal is for your shampoo routine to be second nature.

5. The Final Stage of Natural Hair Growth

Congratulations! You have made it to the last stage of your natural hair growth journey. This phase typically lasts 9-12 months and is about freedom. Your hair is growing back everywhere except for the straight pieces on the tips in the front. Unfortunately, this means you still can't wear your hair in curly styles yet. You will have to wait until the straight ends are completely cut off. However, you can do your favorite styles in your sleep once that is done.

You will be much more committed to finishing this process and will encourage and recruit others to grow through this process as well. Once you have completed this journey, you will be a pro at managing your natural hair, the sky's the limit from there!

Chapter Seven

CREATING A PLAN: TIPS FOR YOUR SHAMPOO ROUTINE

IN THIS LESSON, I will provide tips for optimizing your shampoo routine. I'll also suggest some salon tools we use and provide links to these items on Amazon. Your plan should include:

- **Time Management:** Determine how long your routine should take and plan accordingly.
- **Don't Rush:** Take your time and ensure you are thorough with each step.
- **Re-Shampoo:** If you don't plan on styling your hair immediately, consider re-shampooing it before styling it later in the day.
- **Dedication:** Stay committed to your routine until your hair is complete.
- **Planning Ahead:** Plan your hairstyle the day before or well in advance to save time and reduce stress.

Please check out the link directory for more information on Synergi Products and other resources.

STEAM TREATMENTS: TIPS FOR STEAM TREATMENT

- To get the best results, apply Replenish Deep conditioner and Rose oil to the scalp before steaming if you have very dry hair.
- You can shampoo either before or after steaming your hair.
- Most people prefer to shampoo in the shower.
- Be careful not to steam your hair more than once a week.

Tips for Dry Scalp or Dandruff Flakes

- To alleviate dry scalp or dandruff flakes, apply shampoo directly to your scalp before shampooing. Let it sit for up to five minutes, then rinse it with water. This method will leave you with a hydrated scalp.

Consider These Tips for Detangling Hair Effectively

- To make the process easier, detangle your hair before shampooing. However, some people may find detangling their hair while in the shower easier.
- Avoid using small combs, which can cause breakage and damage your hair.
- Instead, use a wide-tooth comb or a detangle brush for the best results.
- Always detangle your hair before removing any protective styles.

Helpful Tools for Your Hair

- **Shampoo Brush:** This tool helps to stimulate the scalp, loosen any dead skin cells, and clear away product buildup, all while increasing blood flow.

- **Detangle Brush:** The Glide Thru brush takes out tangles without yanking or hurting and can easily be held in your palm.
- **Wide Tooth Comb for Curly Hair Wet:** Use this comb to tease and smooth frizzy or thick hair.

Tips for Young Children's Haircare

Here are some helpful tips for parents looking after their children's hair:

- Use goggles when washing hair to prevent soap or shampoo from getting into their eyes.
- Consider using a shampoo hose with a gentle nozzle perfect for washing hair at the kitchen sink.
- Apply shampoo directly to dry hair and spray with water for particularly stubborn product buildup. Allow the shampoo to sit for a couple of minutes before rinsing.
- Tender heads can be challenging to cleanse, but removing buildup will make the hair much easier to manage.

PROPER TECHNIQUE FOR SHAMPOOING YOUR HAIR

Follow these tips for the best results:

- If you visit the salon twice a month, shampoo your hair during the off week when you're not seeing your stylist.
- If you visit the salon weekly, it's best to shampoo your hair on the day of, or the day before, your salon appointment.
- If you wear wigs, try to shampoo your hair underneath the wig as often as possible. Unbraid your hair, wash and condition it, then re-braid it. If you wear it out under a cap, shampoo your hair as often as you shower.
- If you have a weave or braids, shampooing your hair regularly is not recommended. However, continue reading to learn what to do once you remove your hair.

- Avoid digging or scratching your scalp with your nails. Instead, use the balls of your fingers to apply pressure and stimulate blood flow.
- If you have short hair, you can shampoo your hair as often as you shower.
- Shampoo your hair as many times as necessary to get it clean.
- Make sure to create a nice, rich lather.
- Rinse your hair thoroughly until it is squeaky clean.

TIPS FOR CONDITIONING YOUR HAIR IN THE SHOWER

- Apply conditioner to your hair while in the shower.
- Remember not to leave the conditioner on for over two minutes, which could lead to product buildup.
- The primary purpose of using conditioner is to make your hair manageable, not to style it.
- Comb through the conditioner and detangle your hair while still in the shower.
- Rinse your hair thoroughly until all the product is removed. Rinsing can be therapeutic for your hair.
- Consider doing a cold-water rinse to close the cuticle and pores on your scalp, adding luster and shine.
- Shampooing your hair and applying conditioner is still recommended if you do a steam treatment.
- Apply Synergi Restore Leave-In, as it does not build up on your hair.
- Avoid sitting under a dryer as it takes too long.
- Do not put on a plastic cap and leave it on all day. Conditioner coats the hair, and it's best to avoid that.

Blow Drying Tips and Tools

When blow-drying your hair:

- Divide hair into sections and use hair clips.
- Ensure that the hair is as wet as possible.

- Blow dry in a straight direction and mold hair into the desired style.
- Apply a quarter-size glaze before blow drying while the hair is still wet.
- Cut ends into an even shape.

Blow Dry Comb Tools

- The Conair PRO SilverBird Turbo Hair Dryer is a professional salon hair dryer.
- Remove the comb for better results.
- Store it properly after each use to prolong its lifespan.
- A universal comb attachment fits most blow dryers.

Diffuser

- Attaching a hair diffuser to the end of a hair dryer provides volume and lift.
- Dries curls with indirect heat.

Multipurpose Hair Clips

- It helps organize hair while showering, styling, or on vacation.

Other Tools

- 3-way comb.
- Hooded dryer.

FLAT IRONS AND ACCESSORIES: A COMPREHENSIVE GUIDE

Flat irons are a popular tool for achieving sleek, straight hairstyles. Here are the three main types of flat irons and how they differ:

- **Titanium Flat Irons:** These flat irons are the best at conducting heat and provide consistent heat at varying temperatures.
- **Ceramic Flat Irons:** These flat irons offer consistent results in less time, protecting your hair from heat damage. They also heat quickly.
- **Tourmaline Flat Irons:** These flat irons add shine to your hair by retaining moisture and using reduced heat.

In addition to flat irons, there are a few accessories that can help you get the most out of your flat iron:

- Flat Iron Ear Protectors.
- Flat Iron Gloves.
- Rat Tail Combs.

When getting a silk press, remember these essential tips:

- Straighten your hair before curling it.
- Do not apply oils or creams to straighten your hair.
- The goal is to rebuild your hair, so avoid adding products that increase the temperature.
- To lay your edges or mold your hair, apply mousse after straightening and tie it down immediately with a wrap or scarf.

ESSENTIAL TOOLS FOR PERFECTING YOUR HAIRSTYLE

No hairdo is complete without these finishing tools:

- **Hair Pick:** Perfect for lifting the roots and creating fuller-looking hair, especially for curly styles.
- **Donut:** Ideal for creating a polished bun or updo.
- **Hair Ties:** These are a must-have for keeping your hair secure and in place.
- **Hair Combs:** There are many combs to choose from, but always pick the one that works best for you.

Here are my top three favorite tools:

1. **Shampoo Brush:** This brush stimulates the scalp, removes dead skin cells and product buildup, and increases blood flow.
2. **Detangle Brush:** This brush glides through hair without pulling or hurting, making it easy to remove tangles.
3. **Wide-Tooth Comb:** Perfect for curly and wet hair, this comb helps tease out frizz and smooth thick hair.

Chapter Eight

BEST TIME OF YEAR TO GROW OUT YOUR HAIR

DISCOVERING THE BEST SEASON TO BOOST YOUR HAIR GROWTH JOURNEY

IN THIS SECTION, we'll delve into how different seasons affect hair growth and why it's important. Regardless of when you begin or the duration of your natural hair journey, it typically takes 12 months to achieve a full head of hair. From the 0–3-month stage to the 12-month mark, the season in which you start your journey is ultimately the season in which it will end.

Starting your hair growth journey in particular seasons has its own set of advantages and disadvantages. This lesson helps you plan and anticipate potential challenges to prepare for the process properly.

JANUARY-MARCH:

- Shampooing often can be difficult because of the weather.
- Spring: You will become better at shampooing.
- Summer: It will be tough to manage your hair.
- Winter: Your winter might be challenging but will be your last hard winter.

BENEFITS OF STARTING SHAMPOOING IN SPRING AND CONTINUING THROUGH SUMMER AND FALL:

- Spring is an ideal time to shampoo frequently due to the weather and a sense of renewal.
- With consistent practice during the summer, shampooing will become second nature, making it easier to maintain into the fall.
- By training yourself to shampoo regularly over the summer months, you'll be well-prepared to start the process again next year.

TIPS FOR MANAGING YOUR HAIR IN COLD WEATHER:

Colder seasons can make it challenging to shampoo your hair frequently. The fall, in particular, can be comparable to the winter months. However, the good news is that you can conceal your hair under hats or scarves during this time. Here are some takeaways to consider:

- If you're apprehensive about shampooing your hair in cold weather, try using a hooded dryer or diffuser.
- Remember that not everyone is bothered by shampooing their hair during the colder months.
- It's crucial to assess how to manage your hair throughout each season, as each presents unique challenges.

- Don't limit yourself in your hair care choices. Be open-minded and adaptable to find what works best for you.

Just be aware that winter can be harsh on your hair, especially if you're already six months into growing it out.

Chapter Nine

MY GO-TO STYLES

HAIR IS a crucial aspect of fashion, and having a range of styles is essential. Everyone has unique features, so why not highlight them with various hairstyles? In this article, I'll share my personal go-to styles and provide insight into the time and tools required for each style. As seasons change, so can your hair–be prepared to experiment with different variations of these styles for a fresh look all year round.

GO-TO STYLE #1

- This style takes less than 10 minutes and is incredibly easy to pull off. Any ponytail will do, and it's perfect for day two or three if you don't feel like shampooing.

GO-TO STYLE #2

- I can gauge how my hair will look throughout the day. Although it may start looking fine, I can finish the day with a frizzy mess. I base my look on what I want my hair to look like on that day, how much product I have available, how much time I have to invest, how active I am, the weather, my schedule, and how long my day is. This style is also easy, and sometimes, I can take my hair out of the ponytail and wear it out if I'm lucky.

- Finger curls take me between 10 and 20 minutes to do and 10 minutes to dry. When I do this style, it looks better by the end of the day. The more detail I put into this look and the more time I take to do it, the better it looks. There are levels to this style, including how much product I use, whether I use glaze and mousse, just mousse, how rushed or how much time I took to do it, how early I did it versus later in the day, and what plans I have in the evening determine how much effort goes into styling it.

GO-TO STYLE #3

- I don't often straighten my hair because I prefer it curly. Straightening my hair too much for too long affects my curly looks. My straight style doesn't last long and will not last through a workout. Even though it's pretty and flows well, I'm not willing to do the necessary work to keep my hair straight regularly. It's only for

special occasions, and I prefer it when
it's done in a salon because it lasts longer.
- I can do my hair in many styles with rollers. Although these styles don't last as long, I still resort to style 1 for whenever, style 2 for most occasions, and style 3 for special events.

It's important to note that most people only try to perfect styles 2 and 3 because it takes too long, and they neglect shampooing because of how long the process takes. It's crucial to separate your style similarly to add in the comfort to be able to plan it out better. Your mindset shift should be focused on improving your plan so you can enjoy the process as it grows. Remember that hair will continue to change and adjust as it grows, but trust me, it will get easier and easier, ultimately becoming fun.

Chapter Ten

HOW TO EVALUATE A STYLIST

ARE you struggling to find a hairstylist who specializes in natural hair? Here are some tips to help you find the perfect stylist:

- **Referrals:** Referrals from friends or family can be a great way to find a good stylist. However, remember that everyone's hair is different. With the information in this course, you will be better equipped to understand what you need and get the results you want.
- **New Salon Consultations:** Once you have decided on a stylist or salon, call them to see if they offer consultations. During this appointment, ask questions and be honest about

your expectations. Communication is vital because not everyone has the same views on natural hair.

- **Don't Go Crazy:** Avoid coloring your hair on the first visit. Ask the stylist if your hair is ready for the changes you have in mind and clarify the price. Stylists sell time, and longer processes can add to the cost.
- **Talking to Your Current Stylist:** If your current stylist doesn't specialize in natural hair, you can continue to see them while transitioning. Be honest and upfront with what you need so that if you need to go elsewhere, you can return to them in the future.
- **Shampooing:** If you see your stylist every two weeks, shampoo your hair in between on the off week. If you see your stylist every week, shampoo your hair a few days before your appointment. Regular shampooing can help you understand and love your own texture, which can help you gain confidence and freedom.
- **Make Sure She Shows You How Much Hair She Plans to Cut and Why:** There is a difference between what the stylist cuts and what needs to be cut. If you are transitioning or looking for a particular cut or design, ensure the stylist understands your expectations.
- **Energy:** Assess the energy between you and your stylist during the consultation. Sometimes, we feel we are not being listened to or dismissed. Other times, the person might come across as a good professional, but the interpersonal skills are lacking. Consider whether you're okay with such a relationship or prefer a different dynamic.
- **Hair Crush:** Find a picture of your desired style and show it to your stylist. Avoid showing styles that are in protective styles because your hair will never look like a weave.
- **Conclusion:** Stylists are partners, and they may not understand your process, but that's okay. If you have questions, ask them on Facebook or during the Zoom call. Let's discuss this before your next appointment with your stylist. Remember to get your ends cut straight only.

ABOUT THE AUTHOR

Karen Hill, a highly experienced and passionate hairstylist, has dedicated over thirty-eight years to the hair industry. Born and raised in Columbus, Ohio, Karen comes from a lineage of entrepreneurs, with her father owning a funeral home. However, her true calling and passion lie in the world of hair and beauty. With a natural talent for hairstyling, Karen quickly made a name for herself in the industry. She believes in empowering women through their hair, providing exceptional service, and building a successful salon. Karen's journey inspires others to pursue their dreams and follow their passion.

www.synergisalon.com

facebook.com/synergisalon

instagram.com/synergisalon

tiktok.com/synergisalon

x.com/synergisalon

linkedin.com/in/synergisalon

Printed in the USA
CPSIA information can be obtained
at www.ICGtesting.com
LVHW022305101024
793543LV00035B/1074